Published by Ravette Publishing 2004
Copyright © 2004 United Feature Syndicate, Inc.
All rights reserved.
Licensed by PSL
(www.snoopy.com)

PEANUTS is a registered trademark of
United Feature Syndicate, Inc.
Based on the PEANUTS® comic strip
by Charles M. Schulz.

Printed and bound in Great Britain
for Ravette Publishing Limited,
Unit 3, Tristar Centre,
Star Road, Partridge Green,
West Sussex RH13 8RA

by Cox & Wyman, Reading, Berkshire.

ISBN: 1 84161 197 2

MY FOURTH
2 in 1 COLLECTION
CONTAINS:

MASTER OF
THE FAIRWAYS

MAN'S BEST FRIEND

SNOOPY

(features as)

Master of the Fairways

Charles M. Schulz

ЯR

ALL RIGHT, GOLF FANS, THIS IS IT... THE OLD PRO HAS TO MAKE THIS ONE...

HE'S DOWN TO THE LAST PUTT, AND HE CAN'T PLAY IT SAFE... HE HAS TO GO FOR IT...

© 1977 United Feature Syndicate, Inc.

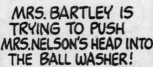

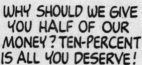

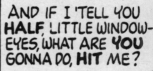

© 1977 United Feature Syndicate, Inc.

7-6

OKAY, YOU CAN PUT THE FLAG BACK IN NOW...

GOOD CADDIES ARE
SO HARD TO FIND
THESE DAYS...

© 1983 United Feature Syndicate, Inc.   7-9

7-29

PLUNK!

THAT WAS A GREAT PUTT! HOW DID YOU EVER DO IT?

NERVES OF GRAPHITE!

© 1983 United Feature Syndicate, Inc.

© 1983 United Feature Syndicate, Inc. 9-5

© 1985 United Feature Syndicate, Inc

2-2

8-17

4-13

SNOOPY

(features as)

Man's Best Friend

Charles M. Schulz

PEANUTS

I APPRECIATE YOUR COMING TO STAY WITH ME, SNOOPY..

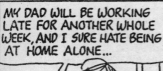

MY DAD WILL BE WORKING LATE FOR ANOTHER WHOLE WEEK, AND I SURE HATE BEING AT HOME ALONE...

I'VE BEEN FALLING ASLEEP IN SCHOOL BECAUSE I'M AFRAID TO GO TO BED AT NIGHT! NOW, I'LL FEEL SAFE BECAUSE I'LL KNOW YOU'RE GUARDING ME, AND...

1-18

Z

HE NEVER SAYS, "BETTER SAVE ROOM FOR DESSERT"

I DID WHAT YOU WANTED...I CALLED THE HUMANE SOCIETY AGAIN

THEY SAID THEIR BUDGET WON'T ALLOW THEM TO GIVE OUT FREE RAINCOATS TO EVERY DOG AND BIRD IN THE COUNTRY...

EVERY TIME THERE'S A GOOD SUGGESTION, SOMEONE BRINGS UP THE BUDGET!

NOPE, YOU WERE WRONG

THERE I WAS, SLEEPING PEACEFULLY...ALL OF A SUDDEN, I THOUGHT I HEARD A HUNDRED-VOICE CHOCOLATE CHIP COOKIE CHOIR CALLING ME...

I WONDER HOW I COULD HAVE BEEN WRONG ABOUT A THING LIKE THAT..

9-29

© 1983 United Feature Syndicate, Inc. 9-13

3-28 © 1984 United Feature Syndicate,Inc.

Other PEANUTS titles published by Ravette . . .

Pocket Books		ISBN	Price
Man's Best Friend		1 84161 066 6	£2.99
Master of Disguise		1 84161 161 1	£2.99
Master of the Fairways		1 84161 067 4	£2.99
The Fearless Leader		1 84161 104 2	£2.99
The Great Entertainer		1 84161 160 3	£2.99
The Great Philosopher		1 84161 064 X	£2.99
The Legal Beagle		1 84161 065 8	£2.99
The Master Chef		1 84161 107 7	£2.99
The Music Lover		1 84161 106 9	£2.99
The Sportsman		1 84161 105 0	£2.99
The Tennis Ace		1 84161 162 X	£2.99
2-in-1 Collections			
Book 1		1 84161 177 8	£4.99
Book 2		1 84161 178 6	£4.99
Book 3	(new)	1 84161 196 4	£4.99
Little Books			
Charlie Brown – Friendship		1 84161 156 5	£2.50
Charlie Brown – Wisdom		1 84161 099 2	£2.50
Educating Peanuts		1 84161 158 1	£2.50
Lucy – Advice		1 84161 101 8	£2.50
Peanuts – Life		1 84161 157 3	£2.50
Peppermint Patty – Blunders		1 84161 102 6	£2.50
Snoopy – Laughter		1 84161 100 X	£2.50
Snoopy – Style		1 84161 155 7	£2.50
Black & White Landscapes			
Now, That's Profound, Charlie Brown		1 84161 181 6	£4.99
I Told You So, You Blockhead!		1 84161 182 4	£4.99

	ISBN	Price
		£9.99
Colour Collections		
It's A Dog's Life, Snoopy	1 84161 179 4	
It's A Big World, Charlie Brown (new)	1 84161 188 3	£9.99
Miscellaneous	1 84161 021 6	£9.99
Peanuts Anniversary Treasury	1 84161 043 7	£9.99
Peanuts Treasury	1 84161 020 8	£7.99
You Really Don't Look 50 Charlie Brown		
		£2.50
Snoopy's Laughter and Learning	1 84161 016 X	£2.50
Book 1 – Read with Snoopy	1 84161 017 8	

All these books are available at your local bookshop or from the publisher at the address below. Just tick the titles required and send the form with your payment to:-

RAVETTE PUBLISHING
Unit 3, Tristar Centre, Star Road, Partridge Green, West Sussex RH13 8RA

Prices and availability are subject to change without notice.

Please enclose a cheque or postal order made payable to **Ravette Publishing** to the value of the cover price of the book and allow the following for UK postage and packing:

60p for the first book + 30p for each additional book
except *You Really Don't Look 50 Charlie Brown* when please add £1.50 per copy, *It's A Dog's Life, Snoopy* and *It's A Big World, Charlie Brown* – please add £2.50 p&p per copy and the two *Treasuries* – please add £3.00 p&p per copy.

Name..

Address ....

....

....

....